Contents

An evil Empire

The Emperor is angry.

He has taken over the galaxy, but some rebels are trying to stop him.

Darth Vader

Darth Sidious

The Emperor is an evil Sith
Lord named Darth Sidious. He has
an apprentice named Darth Vader.

Darth Sidious tells Darth
Vader that the rebels must
be found and destroyed.

Darth Vader obeys his Master.
He sends probe droids to search
the galaxy for the rebels.

The Sith
The evil Sith seek power
for themselves. There are
only two Sith at one time:
a Master and an apprentice.

The rebels

Here are the rebels.
They are hiding in a far
corner of the galaxy on
a planet called Hoth.

Hoth

Han Solo

Luke Skywalker

Princess Leia

Luke Skywalker is a very special rebel. His father was once a famous Jedi. Now Luke wants to become a Jedi, too.

Luke has many friends among the rebels. They are all prepared to fight the Empire.

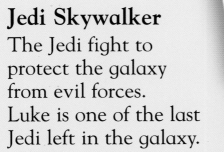

Jedi Skywalker
The Jedi fight to protect the galaxy from evil forces. Luke is one of the last Jedi left in the galaxy.

Rebel base

The galaxy is full of many kinds of planets. Hoth is a cold place, covered in snow and ice. Nobody lives here, which makes it an excellent place to hide.

The rebels have built a secret base. Here it is, hidden in the snow.

The rebels are planning an attack on the Empire.

They need to hurry, because Darth Vader's probe droids are on their way!

Probe Droid

Probe droids are programmed to search for people and objects without being spotted.

Chewbacca

Princess Leia

Wampa attack

There are dangerous creatures lurking in Hoth's snowdrifts. This hairy beast with sharp claws and horns is a wampa.

It has captured Luke and taken him back to its cave. Wampas are carnivores and like to eat people. Look out, Luke!

Wampa cave

Luckily, Han Solo notices that Luke is missing and rushes to rescue him.

Bacta Tank
After freezing in the cold, Luke undergoes medical treatment in a bacta tank. The tank contains special healing liquid.

The Battle of Hoth

Nothing stays a secret from the Empire for long. Darth Vader's probe droids have discovered the rebels on Hoth.

The Sith Lord sends an army to Hoth to destroy the base.

Giant AT-AT walkers march across the snow, firing at the rebels. They trample anything that gets in their way.

Snowspeeder

Rebel pilots try to bring down
the AT-ATs with their agile
snowspeeders, but the enemy
vehicles are too powerful.

AT-AT walker

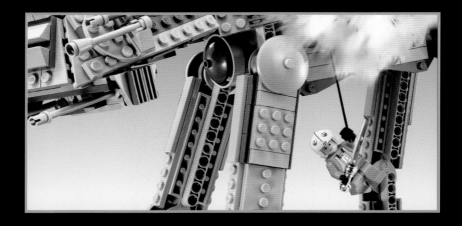

Brave rebels

Luke has a cunning plan.
He climbs up one of the AT-ATs
and destroys it from the inside!

*Millennium
Falcon*

The rebels fight the Empire's army bravely, but they are not able to stop the Empire from blowing up their base on Hoth.

Just in time, Han Solo escapes with Princess Leia in his ship, the *Millennium Falcon*, while Luke zooms off in his X-wing. Where will they go now?

X-wing

Jedi training

Who is this green creature?

On the dark and swampy planet of Dagobah, Luke has found Yoda, the greatest Jedi Master of all time. Now Luke can begin his Jedi training.

Yoda may be small
and old, but he is wise
and strong. He teaches
Luke to control the Force
and resist the dark side.

The Sith use the dark side of
the Force for evil, but the Jedi
believe in using their powers
only for good.

The Force
The Force is a powerful
energy used by the
Jedi and the Sith.
Yoda uses it to lift Luke's
X-wing out of the swamp!

Bounty hunters

Darth Vader is determined to capture Luke Skywalker. He knows that the young Jedi is powerful and wants him stopped.

Dengar

IG-88

These suspicious looking criminals are bounty hunters.

Bounty hunters will work for anyone who will pay them a high price. They specialize in hunting down and capturing people. Darth Vader wants them to capture Luke and his friends!

Boba Fett

Bossk

Boba Fett

This bounty hunter is Boba Fett. He has been promised a large reward if he captures Han Solo.

rangefinder

Slave I

Boba Fett has a ship called *Slave I*. He uses his tracking skills to follow Han Solo's *Millennium Falcon*.

Cloud City

Han Solo and Princess Leia flee to Cloud City. This city floats high among the clouds, and is ruled by Lando Calrissian, an old friend of Han's.

Lando
Calrissian

Lando used to be a smuggler. Can he be trusted to help Han?

Lando doesn't tell Han that Boba Fett followed them all the way to Cloud City. Darth Vader is now waiting for them. Uh-oh!

Trapped!
Darth Vader's fierce stormtroopers surround the rebels. It looks like there is no way out!

Shocking truth

Through the power of the Force, Luke senses that his friends are in trouble. But he arrives too late—and comes face to face with Darth Vader!

Luke puts his new Jedi skills to the test as he duels the evil Sith Lord.

Darth Vader tries to convince Luke to join the dark side. Finally, he reveals the truth: Darth Vader is Luke's father!

Friends to the rescue

What will happen to the rebels next? Han Solo has been captured by Boba Fett. Despite fighting bravely, Luke has been injured by Darth Vader.

Lando Calrissian is sorry that
he couldn't stop Han from being
captured. He manages to escape
Cloud City with Princess Leia.
As they leave, they also manage
to rescue Luke.

Dark times

As Darth Vader returns to the Emperor, it looks like the Empire is stronger than ever.

The rebels have suffered several defeats.

Some of them, like Han Solo, have been captured, but his loyal friends are flying off to rescue him.

The rebels won't give up hope just yet!

Index